THE GEYSER WAT

YELLOWSTONE'S WEST THUMB GEYSER BASIN

2nd edition

JANET JONES

To Liz, Jim & Rachel & Sarah —
Good to visit with you at
Steamboat! Enjoy West Thumb
Janet Jones
31 July 2018

SNOWMOON INK
CODY, WYOMING

Printed in the United States of America

ISBN 978-0-9986808-0-4

SnowMoon Ink
PO Box 311
Cody, WY 82414

Cover Photo: Janet Jones
Inside Photos: Janet Jones unless otherwise noted

Please Note:
Thermal areas are dangerous. Boardwalks do not guarantee your safety. It is the responsibility of the user of this guide to care for his or her own safety and recognize the hazards around thermal areas. The best effort has been made by the author to provide accurate information and suggestions on safety. The author and publisher do not assume and hereby disclaims any liability to any party for any injury, loss or damage caused by errors, omissions, or misleading information in this publication.

I could have dedicated this book to my Grandmother, who lived in Cody, Wyoming (near the East Entrance to Yellowstone) and held my hand so tightly as we walked the boardwalks when I was two, for it was she who first showed the beauty of the thermal features to me.

I could have dedicated this book to my family and friends who have been my tireless cheerleaders as I tackled (and continue to tackle) this amazingly large project.

I could have dedicated this book to the geyser gazers who have sat on the boardwalk next to so many thermal features to learn about their habits and so generously shared what they knew and helped me to learn them better.

But ultimately, I've decided to dedicate it to those who joined me on the boardwalks and kept my enthusiasm for this project strong.

FOR YOU,

the visitor to Yellowstone who wants to know a bit more.

Welcome to West Thumb Geyser Basin

West Thumb Geyser Basin remains an area of fascination and allure for many. Not only does it provide fabulous sunrise views over Yellowstone Lake, but it also contains some of the most beautiful hot springs in Yellowstone National Park.

The West Thumb of Yellowstone Lake formed from a volcanic eruption approximately 170,000 to 200,000 years ago. The caldera it left filled with water and became the "thumb" portion of Yellowstone Lake that's as deep as 430 feet (131 meters). So, West Thumb is a caldera within the larger caldera of Yellowstone.

While the term "basin" usually brings to mind a bowl shape, this area with the boardwalks and thermal features is more of a hillside sloping down to the lake shore. The rest of the "basin" is under water. Some of the many thermal features under water can be seen bubbling or, on rare occasions, boiling when the lake water is still and calm.

This book is a portion of work started in 2005 from a simple curiosity to see how much the thermal features here change. Taking photos in basically the same spot on the boardwalks illustrates the dynamic nature of this geyser basin.

So, whether you're visiting for a once-in-a-lifetime trip or you visit often, I hope this book gives you better appreciation for the unique geology that takes the form of thermal features here in Yellowstone.

If you are intrigued and wish to learn more, please visit

YellowstoneNaturalist.com

What Makes Geysers Erupt?

AIR: Just as water has weight, so does air. Some thermal features are more sensitive to changes in the air pressure than others. Wind can also affect geysers by slightly cooling the surface; this slight cooling may delay eruptions.

EARTH: Geology is the key here. Beneath the geyser basins, you will find loose and broken rock, not unlike the rock you see at the Grand Canyon of the Yellowstone. This loose rock has cracks needed to allow the water to move.

WATER: Hydrothermal Systems (the whole connected system of thermal features) have water involved. Without any water, there are no geysers. Large reservoirs and aquifers lie below the geyser basins.

FIRE: The "hot spot" is a section of magma that rises closer to the surface. The one under Yellowstone creates the heat. As the North American plate has moved over this plume, a trail of previous volcanoes created Snake River Plain ending here in Yellowstone.

The water for the geysers comes, in part, from rain and snowmelt soaking down into the porous rock, but mostly from reservoirs or aquifers known to fuel the hydrothermal system. The hot spot beneath Yellowstone heats the rock which, in turn, heats the water. Hot water rises and fills the cracks and openings in the rock.

Pressure from the weight of the water and air allows the water to become super heated (hotter than boiling). This works in a similar fashion as a pressure cooker. At times this incredibly hot water doesn't even boil on the surface.

Typically, they have a constriction or narrowing in their plumbing. They may have chambers full of water that also help to cause the eruptions.

As the water heats, you start to see bubbles rising. Bubbles are simply pockets of steam. Eventually, you get more bubbles until a large section of water flashes to steam. Since steam takes up more space than water, it pushes any water above it up through and out of the plumbing system, giving us an eruption to enjoy.

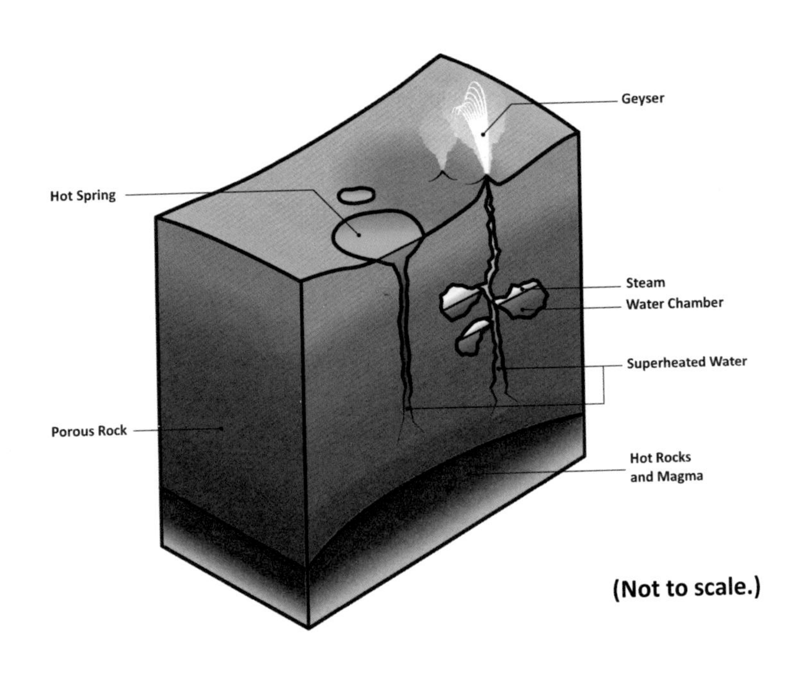

(Not to scale.)

Learn More

While this is a very basic explanation, there are two very well written books that provide more details. Also, stop in the Visitor Centers at Old Faithful and Canyon for some excellent interpretive exhibits.

Geysers: What They Are and How They Work by T. Scott Bryan
Yellowstone's Geysers: The Story Behind the Scenery by Duncan Foley

Names of the Thermal Features

Since the early days of Yellowstone, the thermal features were named for their appearance, behavior or location. Abyss Pool is deep. Surging Spring sends water surging down the hillside. The rule made back then to not name thermal features after people stands today, but a few may stretch the limits such as King Geyser (page 59).

This all works well to help others identify which spring is which until they change their appearance, behavior or even their location. Then it can cause confusion. But thanks to the help of park historian, Lee Whittlesey, many muddlements of the past have been sorted out.

So, when you see a hot spring that doesn't seem to match its name (such as Black Pool which is now a brilliant blue), there's usually a story there (page 62).

To further confuse the whole issue of names, there is no one official system to refer to the myriad of unnamed thermal

Lakeshore Geyser is on the lake's shore.

Black Pool's name doesn't match the brilliant blue color. There's a story to that.

"Footprint Geyser" is often jokingly referred to as "Stay on Walk Spring"

features in Yellowstone. So, authors have either borrowed from one another or simply made up their own.

When working on the Geyser Watch website, I ran into this same problem. So, I decided to use a universal name that lets geysers, hot springs, fumaroles and mud pots to shift and change their nature as they are prone to do. No matter the behavior, they are all thermal features.

Geyser Watch uses:

- **UTF** = Unnamed Thermal Feature
- **"Quotation Marks"** = An unofficial name or nickname

Winter Spring is best seen in the winter when the water level is low.

What's up with the quotes?

You'll also notice quotation marks around some names. This is used not only by Geyser Watch, but also many others to indicate a name is considered unofficial as it hasn't been yet recognized and approved by the US Board on Geographical Names (you can learn more at GeoNames.usgs.gov).

Things to Know

Pack it In - Pack it Out

To help care for Yellowstone, you always need to pack out anything you pack in along your walks on the boardwalk trails. Here at West Thumb Geyser Basin, **there are no trash cans along the boardwalks. So plan accordingly.**

Many people prefer to take a small backpack or bag for garbage.

Amenities

There are only non-flushing vault toilets at West Thumb Geyser Basin. **The nearest flushing toilets are at Grant Village** where you can also find food, lodging and gift shops. A stop at Grant (only a few minutes south) can make your visit to West Thumb Geyser basin more comfortable for everyone.

The Grant Visitor Center is also located at Grant Village. If you notice an eruption, this is where to report it.

Distance, Time and Grades

Most visitors take 45 to 60 minutes to wander through the 1/2 mile or so boardwalk system here at West Thumb Geyser Basin. If you want to work this into your day, know that **Old Faithful Village is about a half hour drive from here**.

If you need to accommodate someone with handicaps or difficulties, know that the steepest grades take you down to the lake along the lower loop trail.

What to Report

Did you see something rare? If you think so, please note the time of any eruption seen and report it to a ranger. They are often on the boardwalks, or you can stop in at the Visitor Center in Grant Village where they'll be happy to learn about what you saw.

Your observations are important and one goal of this guide book is to help you know whether the behavior you see from a geyser or hot spring is typical, unusual or rare.

Icon Codes

Each thermal feature here has an icon at the top of its page to indicate the largest type of behavior seen.

A spring not known to erupt, but it might send up some bubbles.

Small splashes or eruptions **1 to 5 feet tall** have been seen.

Eruptions **5 to 20 feet tall** have been seen from this thermal feature.

Eruptions **20 to 50 feet tall** have been seen from this thermal feature.

Eruptions **taller than 50 feet** have been seen from this thermal feature.

Protect and Enjoy

The National Park Service is charged with protecting the natural wonders here in Yellowstone while simultaneously allowing us to enjoy them. At times this is a difficult balance to achieve.

When thermal features are abused by people tossing in coins or trash, or by foot traffic off the boardwalks or trails, the Park Service may restrict access because their protection wins out over the public's right to see them.

If you see people behaving badly, please *kindly* ask them to correct their behavior. Stay on the boardwalk yourself; they keep both you and the thermal features safe.

Coins (and trash) tossed into thermal features alter the water chemistry and may plug the natural plumbing system, changing the behavior of that spring or geyser. Removing trash and coins requires time from a ranger to carefully pull the items out without causing damage to the feature or to him or herself.

This is Wonderland.

No coins are needed.
Wishes are readily heard here.

West Thumb Geyser Basin

Upper Loop

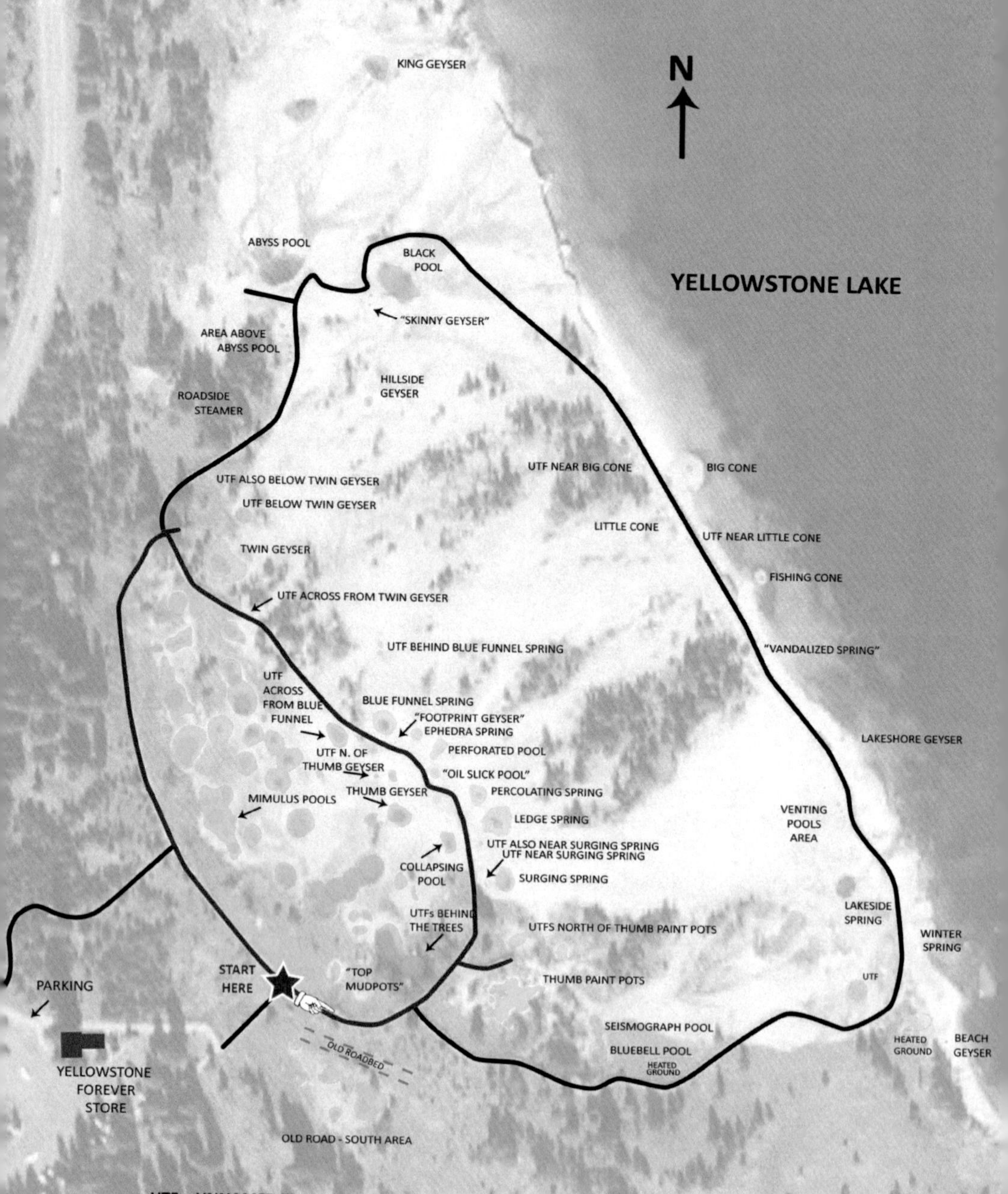

- UTF = UNNAMED THERMAL FEATURE
- "QUOTATION MARKS" = UNOFFICIAL NAME
- APPROXIMATE TIME TO VIEW: 45 MIN
- APPROXIMATE DISTANCE: .5 MILES

“Old Road South Area”

The old road used to go through the higher portion of West Thumb Geyser Basin. It was moved to help protect the thermal features. The boardwalk now takes its place for parts of it. You can see it continue along into areas that are currently closed, such as this area where the old roadbed is now just a straight, raised section of ground to the left of the pools.

When the road did go through here, a boy stumbled and fell into one of these pools, dying from the burns back in 1949. This is yet another reminder of the dangers of hot springs.

This "south area" has no official name, but contains some pools full of water in the spring that dry out in late summer and fall.

4 JUNE 2011

25 SEP 2011

The View From the Top

This is the starting point for both loops covered in this book. The smaller loop has less of a grade, and gives you a chance to see many of the thermal features. The larger loop takes you to the lake's shoreline and includes some of the most stunning pools here. Most of the pools you see from this spot do not have names.

14 SEP 2008

27 SEP 2009

9 AUG 2011

25 SEP 2011

UTFs Behind the Trees

28 JUNE 2005

3 AUG 2014

15 AUG 2014

If you peek behind the tree, you'll see a few unnamed hot springs. Depending on the current water levels, you might see each pool distinctly separate from the others. You also might see the water level high enough to connect the pools at the surface, making them look like a single pool.

But is their plumbing system below ground connected? With this area, it seems there might be some type of connection, but that's not certain.

It's easy to jump to a conclusion with the thermal features at first glance, but continued observation gives insights such as this. This photo documentation project will hopefully yield further clues in years to come.

Thumb Paint Pots

The Thumb Paint Pots behavior sometimes resembles the Fountain Paint Pots in the Lower Geyser Basin, but the actual areas of bubbling mud are on a smaller scale. Some years, the mud pots build into cones that do 'puff' rhythmically. Other years, the mud cones don't even form.

The main pond remains cool enough to allow grasses to grow right up to the edge and sometimes out within the pond itself. The bubbles in this cooler water are formed not from boiling, but rather from carbon dioxide gas rising from deeper below.

As water rises, it brings to the surface various colors of clay, they can look very much like a paint palette.

Areas can look like a paint palette

7 SEP 2014

On Thin Ground

West Thumb, like other geyser basins, is also home for thermal pools that lurk just below the ground and so close to the surface that even elk passing through can break through and open up access to the underground pool.

These openings can develop into something more or can exist for a short time only to be filled in through overflow from other springs or natural weathering.

Near the parking lot side of Thumb Paint Pots, a new opening appeared, probably from an elk passing through. This became one to track through photos just to see what might happen. Over the years, this paint pot became a mud cone at one point, but has since shifted to a small pool.

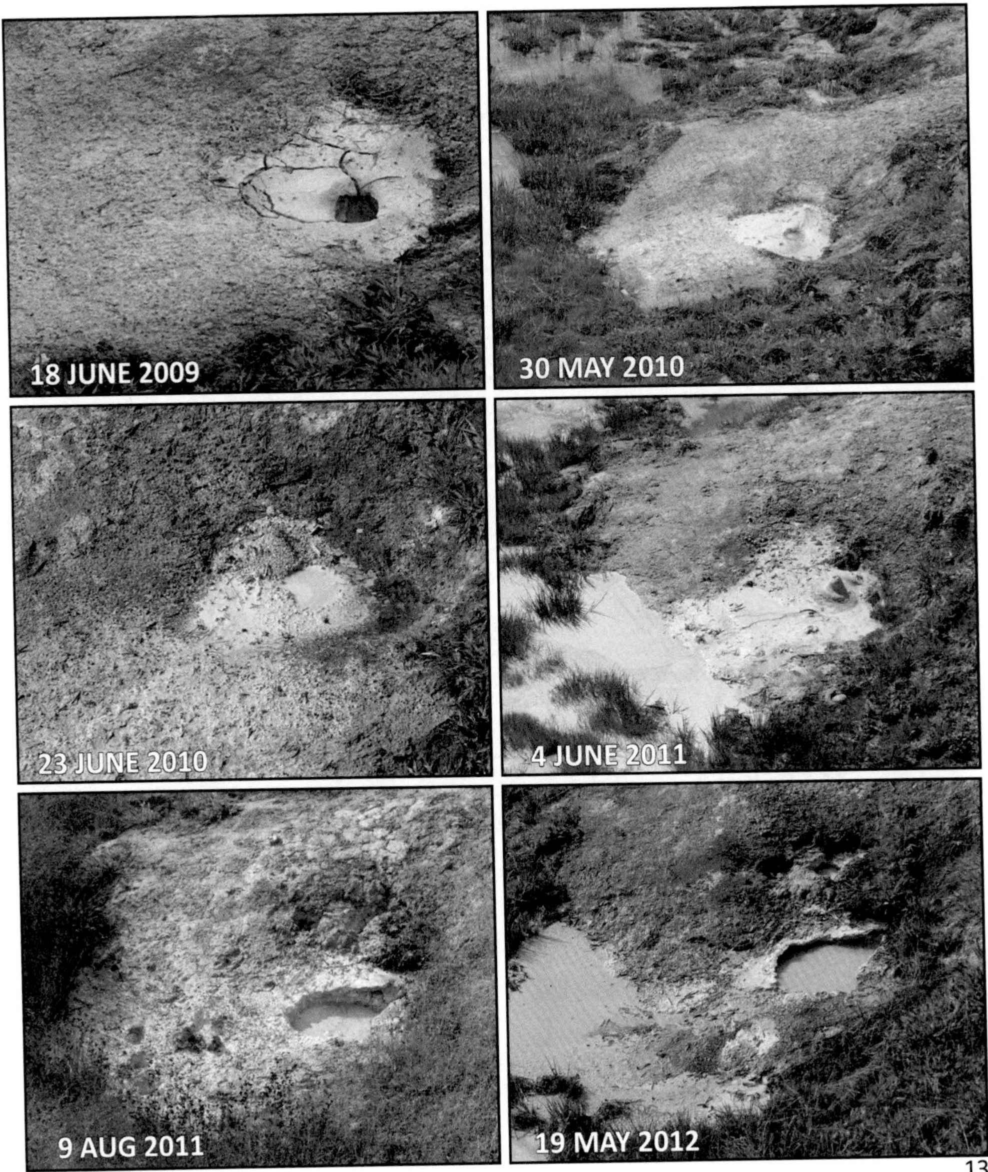

18 JUNE 2009

30 MAY 2010

23 JUNE 2010

4 JUNE 2011

9 AUG 2011

19 MAY 2012

UTF North of Thumb Paint Pots

North of Thumb Paint Pots (to the "left" of the viewing platform) you'll see another pool. This unnamed pool has maintained a milky or opaque appearance since the start of this photographic documentation of West Thumb in 2005.

The story here, though, is about the trees. See the dead ones? Over the small hill lies Surging Spring. The thermal energy shifted to this spring in 2010 and 2011, heating it up and killing some of the trees. Generally, when the ground reaches about 100° F (~38° C) at 1 foot down, the roots become too hot and the trees die. By looking at which ones survived, that gives us an indication of how far Surging Spring's heat can reach.

UTFs North of Thumb Paint Pots

Looking out toward the lake there are two springs that seem to exhibit a wide variety of looks and behavior.

Both of these have been seen bubbling or boiling in the past, sometimes killing the grass and sometimes not. In 2010, a new spring showed up on the hillside to the 'left' of the pools with a couple of others following in later years.

Surging Spring

Surging Spring does erupt, but the weight of the water keeps the splashes small and causes the water in the crater to 'bounce' and send water down the hill in surges. When active, this can happen as often as every 5 to 10 minutes, or it could be as little as just once a day.

In 2010, when the energy increased here, killing many of the trees between Surging Spring and the Thumb Paint Pots, a new thermal feature (on the next page) opened up.

Some years, Surging Spring isn't active at all, but if it's blue and hot, it may surge again.

UTF Near Surging Spring

27 SEP 2009

30 MAY 2010

As stated on the previous page for Surging Spring, a new thermal feature broke through sometime during the winter of 2009-2010. In the first photos above, you can see a stick on the ground in the fall of 2009. In May 2010, this new hot spring showed up beneath it.

New thermal features often show their strongest behavior when they first form and may slowly disappear over time. This one, however, has shown a wide variety of behavior from a bubbling hot spring to a noisy fumarole. Basically, a fumarole is simply a hot spring that has the heat, but has lost the water so it hisses and puffs continually. This differs from a geyser's steam phase which comes after the water during an eruption.

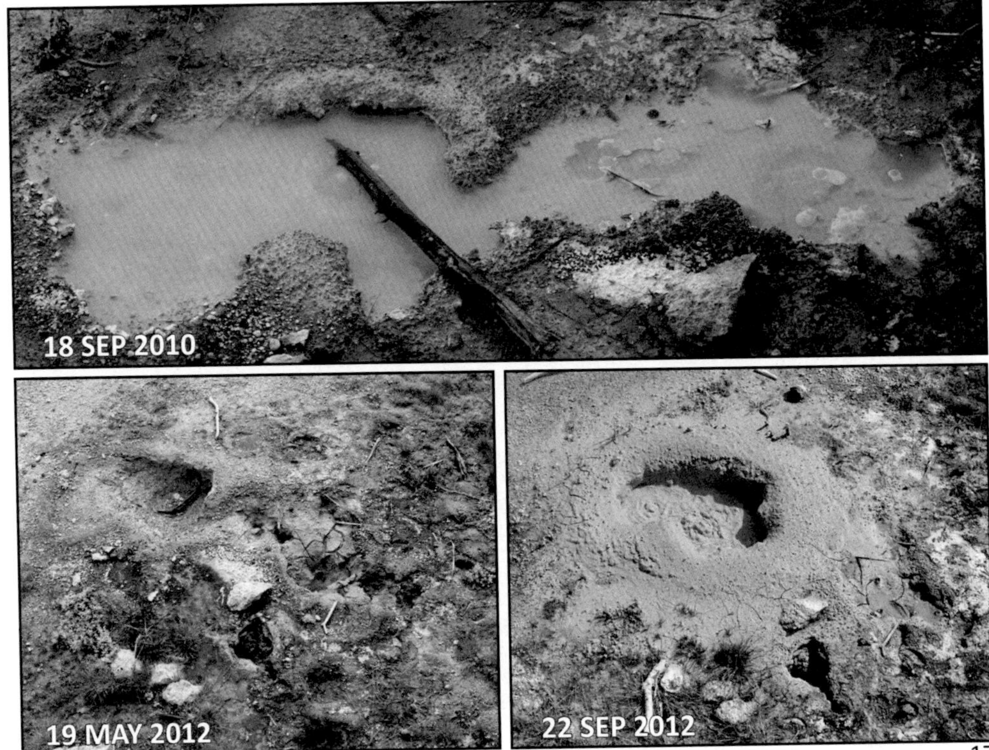

18 SEP 2010

19 MAY 2012

22 SEP 2012

2nd UTF Near Surging Spring

Location Photo

28 JUN 2005

The trouble with so many unnamed thermal features is that it makes them difficult to discuss clearly. This thermal feature is a prime example of this trouble because it, too, is near Surging Spring. Perhaps someday, this one or the one on the previous page will receive at least a nickname.

As with other features in this area, the water levels and temperatures change. This small feature sometimes receives runoff water from Collapsing Pool, but more often is on its own.

When the area is saturated with water, it sits full and bubbling and a few sizzling spots just to the right of it may show.

25 JUN 2013

7 SEP 2014

Collapsing Pool

This pool is named for the collapsed ledges lining the upper part of the pool. Ledges form in a similar way that hard water deposits end up on your shower-head; the bits of minerals in the water stick to the surfaces it touches. As the water level in a spring rises and falls, even in small levels, the minerals slowly build. The thick ledges here collapsed long ago from unknown causes.

This pool usually is a pretty clear blue or green. As with any hot spring, it does have the potential to erupt and this one has been seen erupting. These eruptions can reach anywhere from a few feet to a reported 15 feet, sending a voluminous amount of water out. 2001 was the last year it was regularly seen erupting.

28 JUNE 2005

12 AUG 2009

24 JUL 2010

20 MAY 2014

Ledge Spring

As with other geysers, Ledge Spring needs enough water and heat to have a chance to erupt. A pool full of clear, blue water can indicate that potential.

The eruptions begin with a surge of heavier overflow, and as the water is expelled and the weight lifted, bursts of about 3-5 feet high can occur. Some reported eruptions had only one burst, some had more. After the bursts finish, the water in the pool drops below overflow.

When active as a geyser, Ledge can erupt as often as every 10 to 20 minutes, or it may be up to an hour (more or less) between the eruptions. Please report any eruption seen in this area to the rangers as many people would be interested.

Percolating Spring

28 JUN 2005

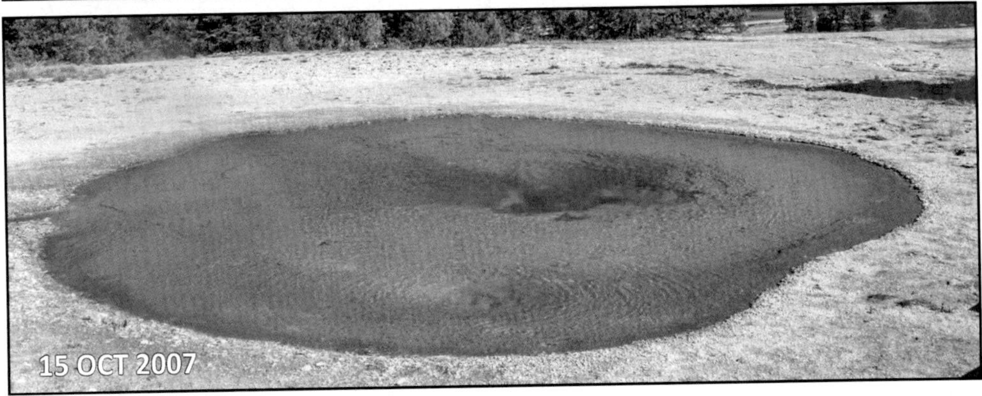

15 OCT 2007

The last time Percolating Spring was seen full and overflowing was in 2007. By 2009, the water level had dropped considerably and from 2010 until 2016, the vent has been empty or holding a small amount of water.

As with other thermal features in this central portion of West Thumb, Percolating Spring has been known to erupt as high as 4 feet when full in the past. In more recent years, it has been seen erupting up a foot or two from a nearly empty crater.

Naturalists here at West Thumb gave this spring its name presumably from bubbles rising that may have reminded them of a percolating coffee pot.

12 AUG 2009

7 SEP 2014

Thumb Geyser

Thumb Geyser sits on the other side of the boardwalk (closest to the parking lot). It often sits below overflow as either a blue or slightly green pool. At least that's how it's looked for most of the past decade.

As with many of the hot springs in this area, Thumb Geyser does erupt. In the past, it has erupted anywhere from 6 to 20 feet high.

It was named in 1964 after the geyser basin itself. Now it may act as a drain for hot springs just behind it.

Other smaller vents in this area have shown eruptive activity that may show one season, but not the next. If you see any eruption, please note the time along with the location or photos and report it.

UTF Next to Thumb Geyser 

The unnamed thermal feature (UTF) to the "right" of Thumb Geyser joins with Thumb Geyser when water levels are high enough. That hasn't happened, though, in many years, but almost did in 2010 as seen on the previous page.

It has shown some activity on its own, as well. In 2008, the water levels were low and splashing inside the crater and sounded very much like a washing machine.

When the water levels sit low in this crater, you can very clearly see the network of holes making up the "plumbing" system that sits just below the surface.

It illustrates the reason for a boardwalk system to safely view thermal features in a geyser basin.

28 JUNE 2005

14 SEP 2008

1 JUN 2015

30 DEC 2016

UTF North of Thumb Geyser

This geyser appeared in late summer 2016 from a vent that sat empty for many years. The eruptions started fairly small and increased in height and changed from a milky color to dark and muddy.

The overflow from the eruptions filled Thumb Geyser and gave insights into possible connections to neighboring springs and geysers.

This geyser can erupt as often as every three hours and has long lasting eruptions (over an hour) to short ones (less than 10 minutes) to heights of six feet.

Many geysers have major and minor eruptions like this one seems to have. Major eruptions generally last long and may have taller bursts, while minor eruptions have less energy to them.

25 AUG 2016

3 SEP 2016

5 NOV 2016

"Oil Slick Pool"

At one point, this pool had a surface glistening with oil, giving it a nickname. While the oily substance (probably just from plant matter) didn't remain, the nickname did. As with many thermal features, a name will stick even though the appearance changes, reminding us of its story.

The last time "Oil Slick" was seen full and bubbling was in 2005. This hot spring joined many others that drained in this central portion of the West Thumb Geyser Basin in early 2014.

Whenever these thermal features fill with water, they may give us a glimpse into which ones might be connected, at least for now.

Location Photo

28 JUNE 2005

3 SEPT 2016

Perforated Pool

28 JUNE 2005

12 AUG 2009

In 2002, Perforated Pool had small one to two foot splashes. In 2005, it cooled enough for microbes to grow. For many years, though, Perforated Pool quietly overflowed and was yet another pretty blue pool in the area.

Early in 2014, Perforated Pool and two neighbors, Ephedra Spring and Blue Funnel Spring all drained completely, followed later by a few others.

In 2001, these same three pools also drained, giving us at least a hint of a possible connection of some sort between these three. Yet more information is needed to prove this theory.

15 AUG 2015

Ephedra Spring

25 SEP 2011

Ephedra brusei, a small brine fly often seen in thermal areas feeding on the microbial mats, gives this hot spring its name. However, in recent years, science has renamed the fly, *Eph**y**dra brusei* to help distinguish it from plants using the spelling Ephedra. The spelling for this spring remains Ephedra.

In years past it also had the name of "Little Blue Funnel" for its similarity to its neighbor a bit farther down the boardwalk.

This spring is part of the trio that has drained together twice in the past, the other two being Perforated Spring and Blue Funnel Spring. These three have also lowered when the UTF Behind Blue Funnel (p. 31) was active as a geyser.

28 JUN 2005

3 AUG 2014

"Footprint Geyser"

As far as research has shown, "Footprint Geyser" consists of these two small springs. While their previous behavior is not well documented, in 2002 they were reported erupting as high as twelve feet one day that summer.

That activity may have shown a link between the two, or they simply may have both erupted together. You can see below the ring of white rock that shows what was likely the extent of the water level. In 2010, the vent farther from the boardwalk pulsed as the water level rapidly rose and fell an inch or two; the vent at and under the boardwalk stayed at the same level with a calm surface.

The railing you see next to this feature was installed in 2012. A young girl was using the side board of the boardwalk like a balance beam (a highly unsafe practice in a thermal area) and lost her balance. A foot went into the spring which was thankfully not boiling hot; neither the girl nor the hot spring were harmed.

Blue Funnel Spring

18 JUN 2009

20 MAY 2014

7 SEP 2014

It's been many years since Blue Funnel Spring has overflowed; the last overflow was seen in 2005. Usually a consistently beautiful blue pool, it occasionally appears murky from an unknown cause. At times hot springs will look murky when rain flows with dirt into a spring. At other times, the cause is unknown.

In early spring 2014, Blue Funnel's water levels dropped along with its neighbors, Ephedra Spring and Perforated Pool. The water also cooled considerably to allow the growth of brownish green microbes.

The clear ring of water showing in the last photo indicates an occasional rise in the water level from what must have been a more consistent level where the microbes flourished.

In December 2016, the water heated up enough to kill the microbes and show as a clear blue once again.

UTF Across from Blue Funnel

This hot spring across the boardwalk from Blue Funnel Spring has remained consistently full since at least 2005, in spite of the drastic differences in thermal features nearby. The only changes seen were in the amount of overflow and the color of microbes growing in the vent, indicating a slight change in temperature.

That all changed sometime during the winter of 2012-2013 when it drained completely, seemingly independent of other features in the area. Clear, hot blue water began to fill it later in May 2013, but since then it has stood mostly empty of water, except for a brief time in 2014 when orange microbes could barely be seen from the boardwalk.

It changed yet again in August 2016 by filling to overflow with two spots of continuously rising bubbles.

By the time you see it, it may have changed again as thermal features seem to want to do.

28 JUNE 2005

30 MAY 2010

27 MAY 2013

UTF Behind Blue Funnel

A little further down the boardwalk on the lake side, there are two vents that have sat empty or steaming for the last decade. But farther in the past it has been seen as a full pool and also erupting as a small geyser that reached 3-5 feet in height.

The last known report of any activity from this thermal feature was in 2000 when it was seen erupting about a foot high.

When erupting, observers have noted that the three pools nearby (Blue Funnel Spring, Ephedra Spring and Perforated Pool) all dropped their water levels, indicating a likely connection - at least at that point in time.

25 SEP 2011

19 MAY 2012

7 SEP 2014

Twin Geyser

Twin Geyser is one of the larger geysers in the West Thumb area. In the 1970s, it was incredibly and reliably active every few hours to heights from 50 to well over 100 feet.

For the past decade, Twin's water level has been down more often than not. Overflow was only seen in 2009, when it looked as though the energy and water levels might be good enough to give us an eruption. By 2015, the vents were empty and only occasionally sending up steam.

When active, the left (north) vent boils as seen in the 2009 photo. Prior to an eruption, the other vent also boils. One vent starts the eruption, and soon the other joins in to erupt to an even higher level.

NPS Photo

15 OCT 2007

27 SEP 2009

UTF Across from Twin Geyser

12 AUG 2009

23 JUN 2010

24 JUL 2010

25 SEP 2011

A bit further down the boardwalk on the parking lot side is another unnamed thermal feature. No information can be found, but it changes constantly.

At times, this hot spring has been seen to dramatically change its appearance in as little as a few days.

Taking photos of this area for the past decade documents that this spring has the distinction of being one of the most dynamic springs along the boardwalks at West Thumb Geyser Basin.

In 2015, the elk started to drink from it. The healthy microbes clearly showed that the bubbling was not from boiling, but rather from gases, as often seen in warm and cool water springs. However, the spring changed again and the elk left.

13 SEP 2015

13 SEP 2015

UTF Below Twin Geyser

From the overlook platform, if you look to the 'left' of Twin Geyser you'll see this unnamed thermal feature. When Twin Geyser's water level is high enough to overflow, it runs into this thermal feature and then runs farther down above Abyss Pool.

What's interesting here are the trees. When the soil temperature increases, it often kills the trees as was seen near Surging Spring. So, did the death of the trees in 2007 signal an increase of thermal energy that showed so clearly in Twin Geyser in 2008-09? Or did the root system on the larger trees simply reach deeply enough to reach heat too hot for their survival?

12 AUG 2009

7 SEP 2014

UTFs North of Mimulus Pools

The entire top area of hot springs have been known collectively as the Painted Pools, and that would be an accurate name for them - for all of them have an inherent beauty all their own.

The next few pages illustrate the dynamic nature of these pools. This gives credence to a more serious study of the possible connections between them and other thermal features in the area.

The walk along here takes you back to where this upper loop started and will also be the starting point for the lower loop. If you aren't interested in the whole lower loop, it is worth your time to head down to see Abyss and Black Pools, as they are arguably some of the most beautiful deep, large pools in Yellowstone.

UTFs North of Mimulus Pools

24 JUL 2010

20 MAY 2014

20 JUL 2014

UTFs North of Mimulus Pools

24 JUL 2010

15 MAY 2013

15 AUG 2014

UTFs North of Mimulus Pools

Mimulus Pools

Mimulus is a plant genus for Monkey-Flowers. Yellow ones (*Mimulus guttatus*), grow near ponds and springs in Yellowstone and likely gave this set of pools its name.

The water level changes, but is consistent within all the pools of this thermal feature. The Mimulus Pools are usually pretty no matter how they change.

Yellow and Pink Monkey Flowers grow throughout Yellowstone. You'll likely see more yellow ones in the thermal areas.

24 JUL 2010

27 MAY 2013

7 SEP 2014

West Thumb Geyser Basin

Lower Loop

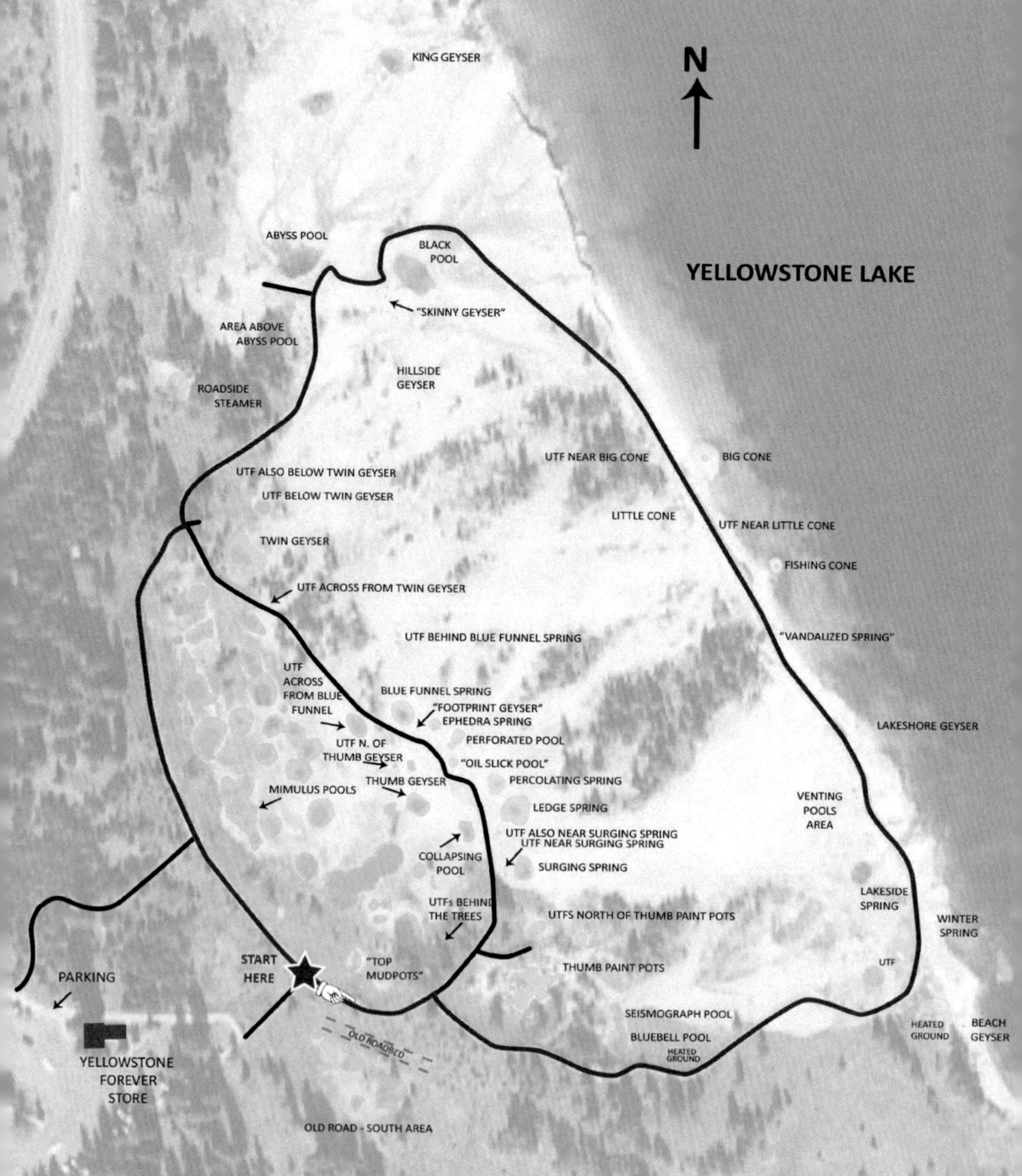

- UTF = UNNAMED THERMAL FEATURE
- "QUOTATION MARKS" = UNOFFICIAL NAME
- APPROXIMATE TIME TO VIEW: 45 MIN
- APPROXIMATE DISTANCE: .5 MILES

Bluebell Pool

Bluebell Pool has been one of the more consistent thermal features at West Thumb, seemingly always the same.

The boardwalk here has changed to give a better view of this blue beauty. Before, the boardwalk came quite close to the pools and photographing this hot spring and its neighbor was quite difficult. This view is no longer accessible. The new boardwalk gives a better overall view of this area and has made Bluebell Pool one of the stars of the social media world.

Named in the 1950s for the way it resembles a mountain bluebell, this spring and its neighbor (Seismograph Pool) have also been known as "The Blue Pools."

23 JUN 2010

30 MAY 2015

Seismograph Pool

12 AUG 2009

4 JUN 2011

While Seismograph Pool may share water with Bluebell Pool on the surface, the two thermal features are decidedly not connected underground. While Bluebell Pool has remained remarkably consistent in its appearance, Seismograph Pool changes temperature and its appearance frequently.

The name Seismograph came about in 1961 by local naturalists. A seismograph measures earthquakes, and it's highly likely that the name for this pool referred to the changes seen here due to the large 1959 Hebgen Lake earthquake.

As was stated before, the views in these photos are no longer accessible.

Area Below Bluebell Pool 

This section of the new boardwalk (as of 2014) curves around an area where a hot spring lies below ground. The park places boardwalks as carefully as possible to both protect the thermal features while also allowing visitors to gain safe access to see them.

The warmer ground allows different vegetation to grow, with the hottest spots being left bare.

This particular hot spring may break through one day, or it may simply sit like this for many years to come, but it is an area to watch.

7 SEP 2014

25 SEP 2014

UTF Above Lakeside Spring

30 MAY 2010

9 SEP 2015

9 SEP 2015

This hot spring (really a warm spring) often has lots of elk hoof prints around it, as they come here for water despite the fresh lake water being so close.

Many of the elk in Yellowstone have heavier or denser bones than those living in other areas in the west due to drinking the mineral-rich water.

Elk are often seen in the West Thumb and Grant Village area. At times, portions of the boardwalks are closed in the spring due to the aggressive cow elk with calves nearby. If you see elk trying to cross the boardwalks, please give them the 25 feet (~8 meters) required here in the park.

9 SEP 2015

Beach Geyser

When the water levels are low, Beach Geyser has the chance to be seen. And now that the boardwalks have been raised, we have a better view of the vent here.

Beach Geyser appeared on the scene in 1975, and was named because of its location. It has been reported to erupt as high as 4 to 6 feet in the past. Little is known about this small feature, but since the boardwalk here was raised, it's been seen producing heavy steam on a few occasions. If you happen to see an eruption, take some photos, note the time and report it to the rangers.

Area Above Winter Spring

This area above Winter Spring could also have been the location of part of the old dock at West Thumb. Park managers learned over the years that structures in thermal areas can cause the heat to rise beneath them. They act in a similar fashion to a lid added to a pot of boiling water that traps the heat so it boils harder.

The thermal heat here increased in the summer of 2009, and killed the grass in an almost perfect rectangle, typical of man-made structures.

Since then, the area has had water rise and create some small hot springs. The energy has waned, but this continues to be an area to watch to see if anything more develops.

14 AUG 2009

24 JUL 2010

25 SEP 2014

Winter Spring

Winter Spring received its name in 1974 because its steam shows so well on cold winter days. It's also easiest to see this thermal feature when the water level of the lake is lower as it is during the winter and early spring.

During the summer months, it's covered by the higher water level of the lake. The warmer water from the hot spring provides an environment where the fish can thrive. And where fish thrive, birds often dine.

In the early days of the park, before the rarity of thermal features was really understood, the dock came up here on the "right hand" side. The dock, and many of the facilities offered here at West Thumb were shifted to Grant Village.

15 OCT 2007

12 AUG 2009

Birds often fish here

Lakeside Spring

There are only two records (so far) of Lakeside Spring having eruptive type activity. One in 2002 simply states that it was seen post-eruptive. This could include anything from a lower water level to a washed area or dislodged microbial mat, or any combination.

In 2014, a ranger reported seeing the water on Lakeside Spring surge up to about 2 feet high and 'bounce' - not really a bursting eruption, but as though it was trying for bursts and just didn't have enough energy to lift the weight of the water. In 2015, small bursts were seen when it had a muddy appearance.

If you happen to see any decent splashes, note the time and tell a ranger.

Venting Pools Area

This area has many small bubblers but is ever-changing. When the hot springs and geysers along the middle boardwalk are full and overflowing (particularly Surging Spring), the water washes down here, filling some of these thermal features with rocks and debris, effectively closing them off. Thermal energy remains, though, and seeks a way to the surface and will reappear, but perhaps not quite in the same location.

A few of these springs have escaped the deluge of water from above and may persist. None have formal names, and it is not yet clear exactly which ones were originally referred to as the "Venting Pools" or even if the original springs still exist.

Venting Pools Area

This little unnamed opening caught a bit of attention in 2006 since it at least overflowed enough to carve out the runoff channel in the rocky debris. Long waits didn't produce much insight, though, until 2009 when the water in this small hot spring rose and fell cyclically, and occasionally splashed a bit of water out.

The runoff channel looked fairly similar until 2011 when Surging Spring up above began to surge again. By 2014, the water from Surging Spring threatened to wipe out this this feature completely.

24 JUL 2010

13 OCT 2006

18 JUN 2009

25 SEP 2011

25 SEP 2014

Venting Pools Area

Lakeshore Geyser

NPS historic photo

Juvenile Fish

12 AUG 2009

20 MAY 2014

13 SEP 2015

Lakeshore Geyser is another thermal feature often covered by the lake water during the summer months. The cold water drowns out any hope of an eruption, but the vent with its warmer microclimate acts as a fish hatchery and juvenile trout (known as fingerlings) often thrive in the larger vent throughout the summer.

Lakeshore Geyser can sit quiet for years, but has also been active as often as every half hour. Taller eruptions come from the smaller vent, and can reach from just a foot or two or as high as 20 to 25 feet, though the taller eruptions have not been seen in many years.

If you happen to see a larger eruption, note the time and report it to a ranger.

“Vandalized Spring”

This hot spring right next to the boardwalk has been and continues to be abused by many thoughtless visitors. Rangers regularly remove trash, gum and coins from this hot spring unofficially known as “Vandalized Spring.”

In 2011, due to above average runoff from the snowmelt that winter, the level of the water in the lake rose high enough to cover this hot spring, scouring out the microbial mat somewhat. Since that time, it has been orange with perhaps a touch of green and with a steady stream of bubbles rising on one side. It makes one wonder what, with a bit more care, this hot spring might look like.

Please pack out all you bring with you along the boardwalks.

12 AUG 2009

9 AUG 2011

Fishing Cone

In earlier days of Yellowstone's history, people weren't aware of how fragile and rare the thermal features were. Back then, Fishing Cone became famous as a "Fish Pot" where a fisherman could catch a fish in the lake and cook it while still on the hook by simply turning around and dipping it into one of the hot springs along the edge of the lake. This practice is no longer allowed and, anyway, it gives the fish a sulfur flavor that's not very appealing.

During much of the summer, it is underwater from runoff in June until the water levels lower again, usually in late August.

A side vent has small eruptions that reach a foot high some years.

Historic Postcard

12 AUG 2009

19 MAY 2012

15 AUG 2014

UTF Near Little Cone

27 SEP 2009

Walking along past Fishing Cone, many visitors miss this tiny thermal feature. It's pretty much an area where the water bubbles up through the broken sinter rock. In fact, it may disappear completely as has happened with other small bubblers along the shore of the lake. Rainstorms can wash rocky debris down while waves from high water years can push rocky debris up. If the thermal energy pauses at all, If the hot spring pauses or stops, this spot may no longer show there's thermal energy here. But its very likely the thermal energy will continue to work its way to the surface somewhere in the area.

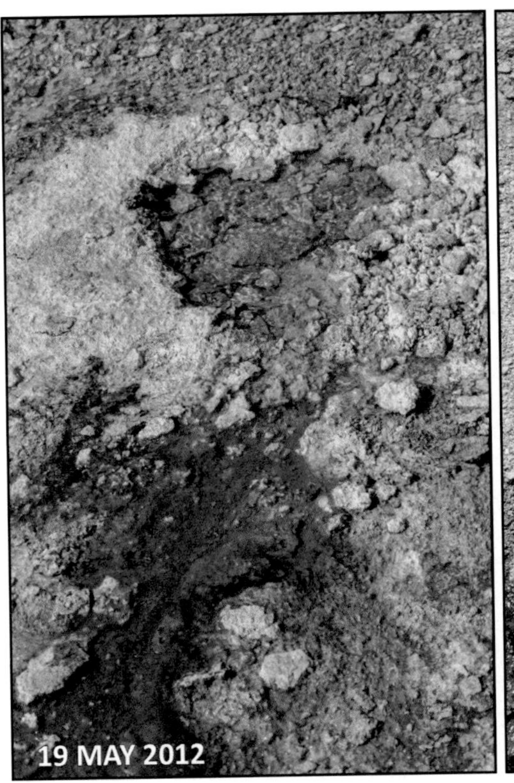

19 MAY 2012

15 AUG 2014

Little Cone

On the uphill side of the boardwalk, you'll see a hot spring at the top of a small cone. The shape of the mound looks very much like the larger version that sits just a bit farther down the boardwalk (shown on the next page).

Little Cone regularly sends up small bubbles that break the surface of the pool, but the main thing to note is the amount of overflow running down the side of the cone.

9 AUG 2011

7 SEP 2014

Big Cone

A short way farther along the boardwalk, Big Cone sits out into Yellowstone Lake. During times of high runoff that raises the water level of the lake, Big Cone usually sits just high enough to keep from being completely submerged. The top photo shows how the water levels can even run past the boardwalk during the spring runoff in high snowpack years.

At times Big Cone boils vigorously, but this is about the closest to an eruption that has been seen. The amount of overflow does seem to increase and decrease at times.

A seep of water comes out from the boardwalk side of the cone, but doesn't show every year.

UTF Near Big Cone

As people walk along the shore of Yellowstone Lake, they may miss this tiny little unnamed bubbler. Despite its small size, it also shifts and changes its look slightly. At times it hardly bubbles, and overflows gently with a temperature cool enough to allow orange and green microbes to grow near the vent. It has also heated up and bubbled a bit more strongly but usually the bubbling only reaches a few inches high.

Over the years, the silica rich thermal water has sealed the surrounding rock together to form a tiny cone. In the years to come we'll know if this little thermal feature might persist long enough to receive a nickname.

Keep an eye out for Mountain Bluebirds and Tree Swallows that nest in this area each year.

30 MAY 2010

7 SEP 2014

25 SEP 2014

King Geyser

King Geyser has no direct access. It's an irregular performer that has been active in the past few years.

How it received its name is not fully known, but it could have been named by someone accompanying the Crown Prince Gustaf of Sweden when visiting in 1926.

Before an eruption, boiling occasionally increases. One of these boils eventually builds into an eruption that may reach anywhere from 6 to 15 feet tall and can last for 5 to 10 minutes. As the eruption continues, the water level lowers in the crater until it drains out of sight and all steam ceases.

If you see an eruption or an empty crater, note the time and let a ranger know.

"Skinny Geyser"

"Skinny Geyser" received its informal nickname when someone watching an eruption made a comment about the slender jet. Due to the distance from the old boardwalk, it hasn't received much attention, but now with the new location of the viewing platform for Black Pool, this small geyser along with its unnamed neighbors will certainly benefit.

At the writing of this guidebook, we don't have much of an idea of how often "Skinny" erupts, but it is seen erupting up to 10 feet high at first before quickly shifting to a steam phase, with the entire eruption lasting about 3-4 minutes.

If you see an eruption, please note the time and report it to a ranger to help us all know more about "Skinny's" behavior.

UTFs Near "Skinny Geyser"

Near "Skinny Geyser" are a few pools that have mostly been observed from afar. Now that we can get a closer look, we will get to know them much better.

One of these actually may have a name - North Star Geyser. It might be the thermal feature shown in the top photo.

The water level in the thermal feature shown in the middle two photos rises and falls about every 10 to 15 minutes, but unlike some of its neighbors, currently does not splash.

The bottom left photo shows a few small openings that were sizzling at least at the end of the Summer 2014 season.

The bottom photo shows two springs; the lower one with heavy sinter deposit has existed for years. The other is newer.

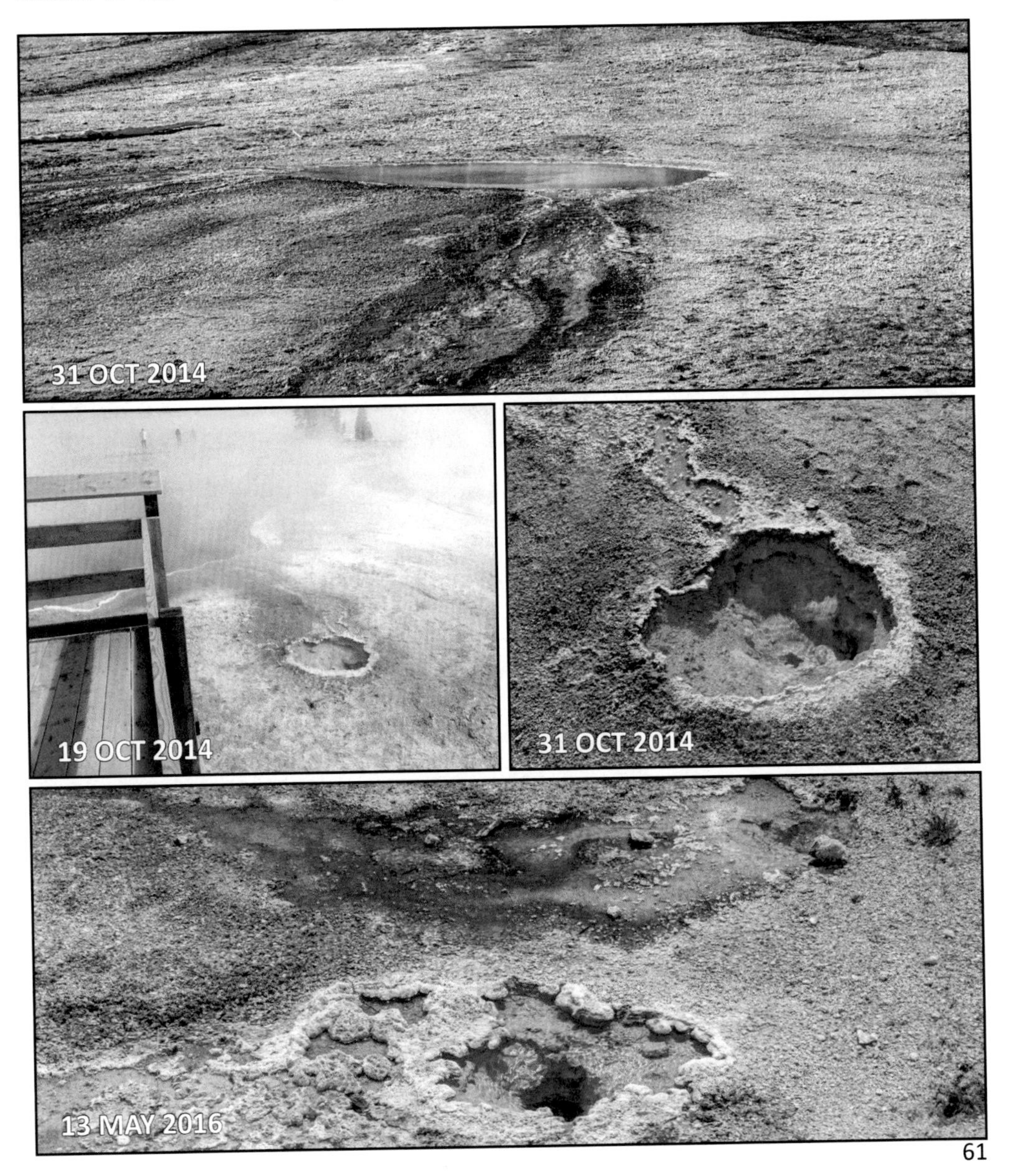

Black Pool

Black Pool is a gorgeous blue, but it used to be so dark it looked black as shown in the photo below.

In 1990, a small vent on the north side of the pool may heated up and sent hot water into Black Pool. This inflow of hot water killed the microbes, allowing you to now see its depth of 35-40 feet.

In 1991, the north vent gained enough energy to erupt and break more of the sinter rock separating it from Black Pool.

During the same time Abyss Pool was active as a geyser, Black Pool's eruptions were large surges of boiling water, rather than bursts.

Bubbles still rise from the north vent but are not indicative of an eruption.

NPS Photo 1978

10 JUL 2015

Abyss Pool

Abyss Pool is one of the stars of West Thumb Geyser Basin. It's been measured to a depth of 53 feet.

For much of the past decade, it has been a luscious green pool. At other times, it has heated up enough to be a clear blue, and has a history of large 100 ft eruptions. These powerful eruptions in the early 1990s happened as often as every 3 hours.

Eruptions usually started with boiling around the edges followed by a sudden surge of water flooding the surrounding area, and then bursts reached 80 to 100 feet. The eruptions were quick, but short-lasting with eruptions anywhere from 45 seconds to 3 minutes.

28 JUNE 2005

11 JUL 2012

15 AUG 2014

Area Above Abyss Pool

A video reference to this area above Abyss Pool mentioned that some of these thermal features may have broken out about the time Abyss had some powerful eruptions in the early 1990s, indicating a likely connection.

When Twin Geyser is full and overflowing, this area is flooded with the runoff, allowing a lush mat of microbes to thrive. Without that overflow water, the microbial mats dry up and deteriorate. As they weather and break down, the debris fills the vents. The heat remains, though, and provides a warmer microclimate in which many plants thrive. If the heat slightly increases, these vents can open up again, either with or without water.

Hillside Geyser

Located behind a few trees, Hillside Geyser has been dormant more than active, but when active it can reach heights of up to 110 feet. Most described eruptions rise to reach between 50 and 80 feet and last about 5 to 6 minutes.

The last reported eruption was clear back in 2002, so we're into the second decade of dormancy for this geyser. When active in the late 1990s and early 2000s, intervals between eruptions could be anywhere from 1 to 8 days. Eruptions began with convection (somewhat of a swirling movement) of the water.

A pair of binoculars can be helpful to watch for convection from the boardwalk. If you see it erupt, note the time and report it to the rangers.

2nd UTF Below Twin Geyser

Not much information exists on this hot spring, though through the years, it has changed its appearance frequently. Between 2011 and 2014, the water level slowly dropped farther into the crater. In 2015, this draining continued at a slightly increased pace. This is yet another spring to watch and see if it disappears over time or comes back to life.

12 AUG 2009

30 MAY 2010

24 JUL 2010

4 JUN 2011

25 SEP 2011

18 JUN 2012

25 SEP 2014

Roadside Steamer Area

The old road used to go along the top boardwalk at West Thumb. Here you can see the old roadbed.

The thermal feature creating the crater in the distance is Roadside Steamer. It has had eruptions in the past that reach anywhere from 3 to 40 feet high. It hasn't been seen to be active in many years, so if you see water erupting from it, be sure to report it.

The more interesting item to note here is the Unnamed Thermal Feature (UTF) visible from the boardwalk. This small hot spring seems to depend mostly on seasonal ground water because it's full of water each spring (occasionally overflowing), and dries out throughout the summer months.

About the Author

Janet is a life-long learner with many interests in the natural sciences. She captures what she sees and experiences in field notes and photos to create entries in her field journals. This book and the companion websites are the natural outgrowth of her background in education and desire to share information with the visitors to Yellowstone - once a teacher, always a teacher.

This personal project of tracking the thermal features in Yellowstone might, at some point, be of interest to scientists wishing to study the shifts of thermal energy in geyser basins. She is passionate about continuing to add to her field journals. It's a reason to simply be outside as often as possible. She invites you to join in as well and find your path to being outside.

Janet lives in Cody, Wyoming where generations of family passed on their love of Yellowstone and the thermal features.

Learn more on about current thermal activity on her website

Suggested Reading

Learning about the hundreds of thermal features can seem daunting. There are many resources available to help you learn more. These are resources I have found helpful. You can find many of them in Yellowstone book stores and online.

Brock, Thomas D. *Life at High Temperatures*. Yellowstone National Park, WY. Yellowstone Association for Natural Science, History and Education, Inc. 1994.

Bryan, T. Scott. *The Geysers of Yellowstone*. Boulder, CO. University of Colorado Press. 2008.

Bryan, T. Scott. *Geysers: What They Are and How They Work*. Missoula, MT. Mountain Press Publishing Company. 2005.

Foley, Duncan. *Yellowstone Geysers: The Story Behind the Scenery*. Las Vegas, NV. KC Publications. 2006.

Geyser Observation and Study Association. *The Geyser Gazer Sput*. Vol 1-30. geyserstudy.org (Newsletter)

Geyser Observation and Study Association. *GOSA Transactions*. Vol 1-11. geyserstudy.org (Journal)

Montana State University. *Living Colors: Microbes of Yellowstone National Park*. Yellowstone National Park. Yellowstone Association. 2013.

Schreier, Carl. *Yellowstone's Geysers, Hot Springs and Fumaroles*. Moose, WY. Homestead Publishing. 2005.

Whittlesey, Lee. *Yellowstone Place Names.* Gardiner, MT. Wonderland Publishing Company. 2006.

Index

Made in the USA
San Bernardino, CA
25 March 2018